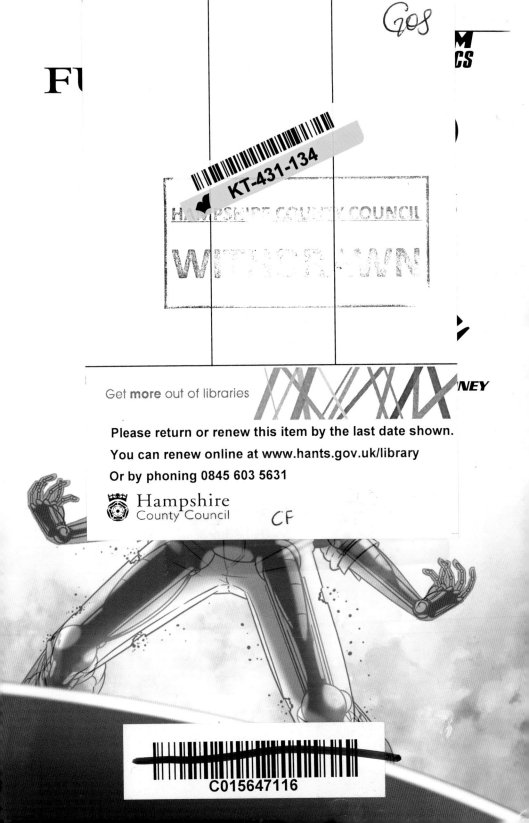

G08

F...

M
CS

KT-431-134

NEY

Get **more** out of libraries

FULL METAL
HERO

There has been a massive explosion in the city. Someone tried to kill the president! The president is safe, but Jet was at the centre of the blast...

First published in 2013 by
Franklin Watts
338 Euston Road
London NW1 3BH

Franklin Watts Australia
Level 17/207 Kent Street
Sydney, NSW 2000

Text © Jonny Zucker 2013
Illustrations © Franklin Watts 2013

The rights of Jonny Zucker to be identified as the author and Dan Boultwood as the illustrator of this Work have been asserted in accordance with the Copyright, Designs and Patents Act, 1988.

A CIP catalogue record for this book is available from the British Library.

ISBN: 978 1 4451 1801 7

Series Editors: Adrian Cole and Jackie Hamley
Series Advisors: Diana Bentley and Dee Reid
Series Designer: Peter Scoulding

A paperback original

1 3 5 7 9 10 8 6 4 2

Printed in China

Franklin Watts is a division of Hachette Children's Books, an Hachette UK company
www.hachette.co.uk

4

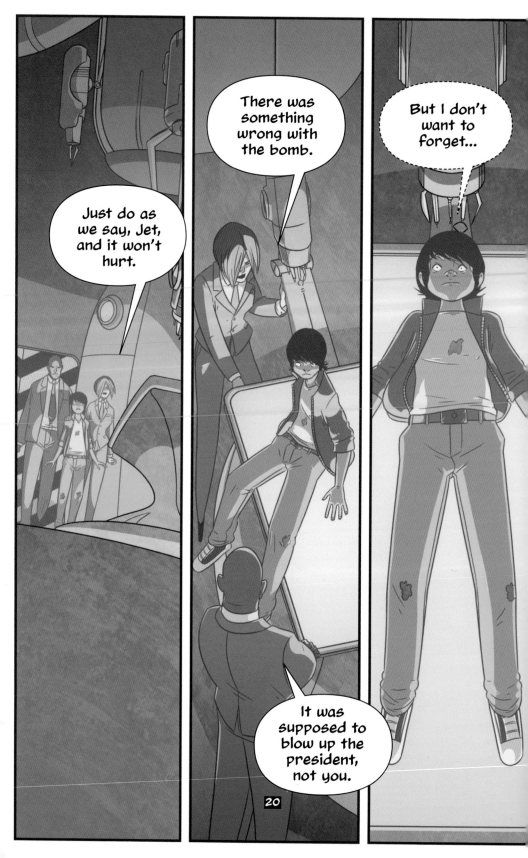

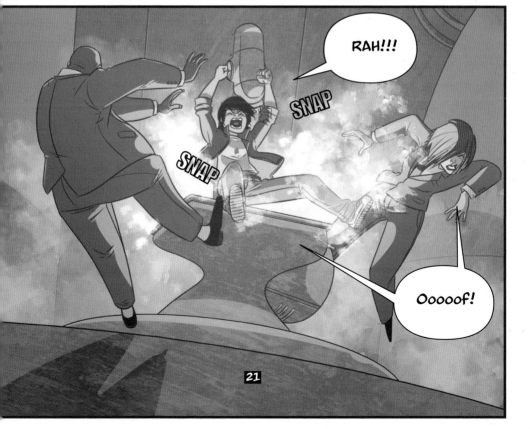

21

About

SLIP STREAM

Slipstream is a series of expertly levelled books designed for pupils who are struggling with reading. Its unique three-strand approach through fiction, graphic fiction and non-fiction gives pupils a rich reading experience that will accelerate their progress and close the reading gap.

At the heart of every Slipstream graphic fiction book is a great story. Easily accessible words and phrases ensure that pupils both decode and comprehend, and the high interest stories really engage older struggling readers.

Whether you're using Slipstream Level 2 for Guided Reading or as an independent read, here are some suggestions:

1. Make each reading session successful. Talk about the text or pictures before the pupil starts reading. Introduce any unfamiliar vocabulary.

2. Encourage the pupil to talk about the book using a range of open questions. For example, how would they feel if they had full metal strength? What would they do with their power?

Slipstream Level 2 photocopiable **WORKBOOK** ISBN: 978 1 4451 1797 3 available – download free sample worksheets from: www.franklinwatts.co.uk

3. Discuss the differences between reading fiction, graphic fiction and non-fiction. What do they prefer?

For guidance, SLIPSTREAM Level 2 – Full Metal Hero has been approximately measured to:

National Curriculum Level: 2b
Reading Age: 7.6–8.0
Book Band: Purple

ATOS: 2.0*
Guided Reading Level: I
Lexile® Measure (confirmed): 320L

*Please check actual Accelerated Reader™ book level and quiz availability at www.arbookfind.co.uk